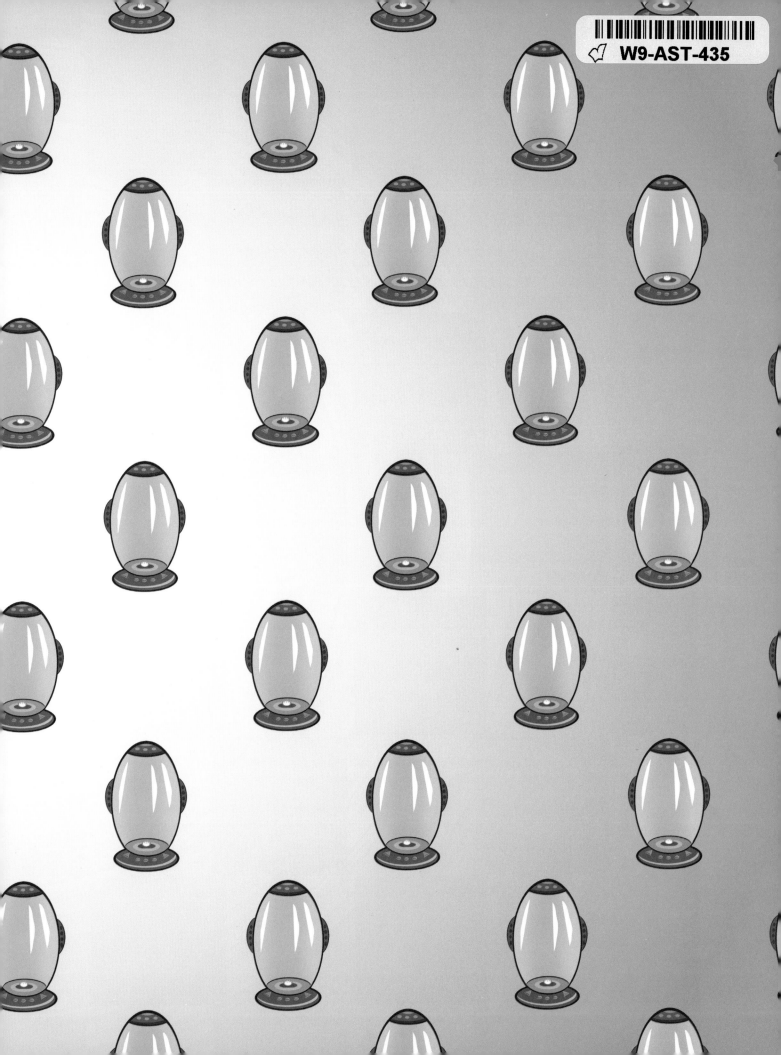

To all of the parents and educators
committed to teaching children
about the benefits of eating fruits and vegetables,
Thank you for your encouragement and support of the
Mitch Spinach mission.

And, as always, for SIF and QLF,
who lead with grace and fervor.

First Edition, Published by Mitch Spinach Productions, Inc.

Printed in the United States
ISBN 978-0-578-08262-2

Library of Congress Control Number:
2011905604

# Mitch Spinach and The Smell of Victory

FIELD DAY

1

SUNCHOKE ELEMENTARY SCHOOL

## by Hillary Feerick & Jeff Hillenbrand
### in collaboration with Joel Fuhrman, M.D.

### illustrated by Andrea Vitali

Mitch Spinach Productions, Inc.

"Good morning, Sunchoke Elementary!" said a crackly-voiced Mrs. Persimmon over the loudspeaker. "We are ready to embark on an exciting adventure together as a school.

Today is one of the greatest days of the year: FIELD DAY! I hope you had a good breakfast and now have an appetite for FUN! Remember, the first, second, and third place teams will receive trophies, and every student will receive a ribbon for his or her participation. All students, please report to your designated areas on the field. Let the games begin!"

"Yeah!" shouted the kids in every classroom.

"Hooray!" shouted Principal Lycopene. "I love field day!"

Out on the field, the Green and Red teams squared off for the tug-o-war. The kids dug their feet into the dirt and pulled the rope as hard as they could.

"This is going to be a close one," said Ms. Radicchio to Mrs. Persimmon. "The Red and Green teams are closely matched."

"Ohhhh! And victory goes to the Green team! Good work by both teams!" shouted Mrs. Persimmon in a booming voice.

"Wow, that Mitch Spinach is strong!" said Max. "I wish he were on my team!"

"I think it's all that cool food he brings to school. Did you see what he ate for lunch yesterday?"

"Yeah. That soup smelled so good. What did he say was in it again? White beans . . . and, I think he called it kale, right?"

"It was DINOSAUR kale. He said it makes him extremely strong and gives him eagle eyes!"

He's amazing! Maybe I could get my mom to make Dinosaur Soup for me," said Max.

"Good idea," Logan agreed.

At the softball-throwing event, Mitch Spinach was standing with his friends, rooting for their team.

"Go Green!" shouted Mitch Spinach.

"You can do it, Yellow!"

"Way to go, Blue!"

All of the kids were cheering as loudly as they could. Each team was awarded extra points for spirit. Mrs. Persimmon loved it when the kids encouraged one another.

Somehow, amidst all of the shouting and cheering, Mitch Spinach heard something. It was Mr. Fava and Becca across the field at the north corner. Becca was telling Mr. Fava that she didn't feel quite right.

"I don't think I have the energy to do the broad jump, Mr. Fava."

Mr. Fava was concerned: "Did you have a good breakfast, Becca?"

"No, actually, I skipped breakfast this morning," said Becca, reluctantly.

At that instant, Mitch Spinach appeared with his space-age looking Nutripak.

"Hi, Becca.  I overheard you and Mr. Fava talking about . . . "

Becca and Mr. Fava looked puzzled.

"From across the field?" they asked.

"Yeah, I thought I heard you say that you didn't get to eat breakfast this morning.  I have one of my homemade super bars in my Nutripak.  It's made of dates, cashews, sunflower seeds, cocoa powder and, of course, my special veggie mix.  It'll give you amazing strength and power!  Would you like to try it?"

"Sure!  Thanks," said Becca.

Becca pulled back the wrapper of the chocolate nut bar.  "Mmmm . . . this is delicious!" said Becca, feeling better.  After a cup of water and a few more bites, Becca was ready to go.

"What a jump!" said Mr. Fava. "Well done!  The Blue team has won this event, thanks to Becca."

"And Mitch Spinach," said Becca as she turned to thank her friend, but Mitch Spinach had already disappeared.

As the day was winding down, Prinicpal Lycopene said, "You did such a great job organizing this event, Mrs. Persimmon. When I was a kid, field day was my favorite day of the year. I remember the excitement we felt when our team won a trophy! You have the trophies and ribbons, Mrs. Persimmon, right?"

"They're locked up in the storage cabinet in the gym. I'll go get them right now. Oh, no! Where are my keys?"

"I don't know," said Principal Lycopene, looking nervous.

"I always have them around my neck. My whistle is here, but my keys are gone! What are we going to do? We have only twenty-five minutes until the awards ceremony. The kids will be incredibly disappointed if they don't get their trophies and ribbons."

"O.K., stay calm," said Principal Lycopene, pulling himself together. "Let's look around on the field to see if we can find them."

Finally, after a thorough search, Mrs. Persimmon and Principal Lycopene gave up.

"I was so excited for the big day," explained Mrs. Persimmon, "I must have dropped them somewhere inside."

"Don't worry, Mrs. Persimmon, I know the perfect person for this job. You just finish up with the field day and round up the kids for the awards in fifteen minutes. Hopefully, we'll have those keys by the end of the grand finale relay race."

"Alright. I hope you—or whoever you have in mind—can find them," said Mrs. Persimmon with a worried look on her face.

Meanwhile, Mitch Spinach was on his way back to join the Green team when a beeping sound alerted him that a message was printing out of his futuristic, computerized watch. Mitch Spinach recognized Principal Lycopene's familiar code on the skinny, red piece of paper. The odd characters on the note told him to report to the gym immediately!

Quickly, Mitch Spinach whispered something in Ms. Radicchio's ear and ran off.

Arriving at the gym two minutes later, Mitch Spinach found his principal, looking upset. "Thanks for coming so quickly, Mitch Spinach," said a relieved Principal Lycopene. "This mission is a race against the clock. We have only fifteen minutes to find Mrs. Persimmon's keys or the whole student body of Sunchoke Elementary AND its principal will be extremely disappointed."

Principal Lycopene recounted the events leading up to the mystery of the lost keys. "I have to get back out onto the field to help Mrs. Persimmon," said Principal Lycopene anxiously. "Do you think you can handle this mystery on your own?"

"Absolutely," promised Mitch Spinach. "I'll do my best to retrace her steps and find those keys."

"I knew I could count on you," said Principal Lycopene before running out the door.

"I'll begin here in the gym," Mitch Spinach thought to himself. "Maybe she sat down at her desk for a minute before going to the office."

Her desk was in perfect order, not a paper out of place. Clipboards for each class and sharpened pencils lined up in a row—but no keys!

Walking to the office, Mitch Spinach kept his eyes glued to the floor, hoping to see the keys, but there were no keys to be found.

Neither the ladies in the front office nor Mr. Habanero had seen Mrs. Persimmon's keys. Mitch Spinach looked under the check-in counter, in the nurse's office, and in the mailbox area. No keys!

Mitch Spinach took to the halls. He paced up and down the hallway leading from the front office to the gym. He checked in the stairwells. He looked under the cubbies outside room 214. No keys!

Finally, Mitch Spinach crouched down and put his head in his hands. "I can't imagine where those keys could have gone! I don't know what I'm going to do. Principal Lycopene will be so disappointed in me. He is counting on me. The whole school is counting on me! I can't let them down," thought Mitch Spinach. "Maybe I need a little refueling, just like Becca this morning."

From the main compartment of his Nutripak, Mitch Spinach took out his high-speed, battery-powered blender. He unzipped a side pocket where he kept his shiny stainless steel shakers and sprinkled a green powder made with spinach, wheatgrass, broccoli, and spirulina into the container.

"These protein-packed super greens will give me the strength and endurance I need to solve this difficult mystery," thought Mitch Spinach.

Reaching into the refrigerated section of his backpack, Mitch Spinach threw in a handful of blueberries, four ounces of water, six juicy strawberries, and ten green grapes. With one whiz of the blender, Mitch Spinach had made a delicious drink to reboot his system.

"Ahh . . . that's better," he said aloud. "Those berries will super-charge my brain and help me focus on finding Mrs. Persimmon's keys. They must be here somewhere!"

Pacing up and down the halls again, Mitch Spinach noticed a strong scent wafting out from one of the closed doors. This door was ALWAYS closed.  It was the door to the faculty room.  No kids were ever allowed in that room.  Who knows what the teachers really did in there—graded papers, perhaps, told jokes, talked about the students, maybe.  One thing was for certain: they drank coffee.  It was the smell of coffee that jogged his memory.

"Mrs. Persimmon always has a cup of coffee in her hands, and she was definitely holding a full cup when the games began. Hmmm . . . maybe she went into the faculty room to fill up her cup before the field day started and forgot to mention it to Principal Lycopene."

Mitch Spinach knocked timidly on the door of the faculty lounge, but no one answered.  He knocked again, a little more forcefully, but there was still no answer.  Mitch Spinach opened the door and peeked inside.  "Hello.  Is anyone in here?"

No one answered, of course, because all of the teachers were out on the field with the kids.  Mitch Spinach was not sure what to do.

"Principal Lycopene asked me to handle this mystery on my own.  I think he'd approve of my going in to take a look around," he thought to himself.

Mitch Spinach tiptoed around the room, noting the comfy leather chairs, the containers of red pens on the table, and the pitchers of water near the refrigerator at the far end of the room. A variety of multicolored coffee mugs labeled with different teachers' names hung on a peg board above a giant coffee urn bubbling and exuding its aroma.

And there, next to the coffee maker, were Mrs. Persimmon's keys! Mitch Spinach was beside himself with happiness.

He grabbed the keys and ran back to the field to meet Principal Lycopene and hand them off.

"Where did you find them, Mitch Spinach?"

"No time to talk now, Principal Lycopene. I'm last in the relay race, and it's almost my turn. Gotta go."

"Thanks!" shouted Principal Lycopene after him.

The Green team was almost finished with the relay race. "Where's Mitch Spinach?" questioned Isabella. "He always seems to disappear. We really need him to win this race. We're neck and neck with the Red team again."

"I know. He's up next, and we need to win this event to take first place," remarked Logan.

Ms. Radicchio assured her students that Mitch Spinach would make it back in time, but even she looked worried.

A minute later, Mitch Spinach arrived, just as his teammate finished her leg of the relay.  He grabbed the baton and jumped into the race.  He was one length behind the last Red team member, but with astonishing speed, he began to pull ahead.

Zooming like a rocket in the last twenty-five yards, Mitch Spinach took the lead and brought his team to victory!

On the way home from school, Mitch Spinach's mom asked how his day was.

"Field day was so much fun!" said Mitch Spinach. "It wasn't easy, but we earned a first place trophy. Principal Lycopene told me, personally, that I did a great job."

"That's wonderful, dear," said his mom.

"Oh, and, by the way," added Mitch Spinach, "Max asked me for the recipe for your Dinosaur Soup. Can you give it to his mom?"

"Absolutely."

# SECRETS FOR PARENTS AND TEACHERS

After reading this book, children ask "Can berries make you think more clearly?" or "Does kale make you super strong and give you eagle eyes?" These and other questions provide a great opportunity to explore the teaching message implicit in the Mitch Spinach mission:

> Natural plant foods contain necessary and even essential components that enable optimal function of the human body, ensure maximum performance, and prevent against disease.

## Can berries make you think more clearly?

Naturally sweet and juicy, berries are low in sugar and high in nutrients. They are full of antioxidants, pigments that give fruits and vegetables their vibrant colors. In fact, berries are some of the highest antioxidant foods in existence and are rich in flavonoids and antioxidant vitamins (like vitamin C). Berries' plentiful antioxidant content is beneficial for preventing heart disease, diabetes, cancer, and age-related decline in brain function. Berries can even reduce blood pressure and inflammation (preventing damage to DNA), prevent tumors from acquiring a blood supply, and stimulate the body's own antioxidants. Berry consumption improves both motor coordination and memory and is linked to improved intelligence with aging. You can use fresh or frozen berries and greens to make delicious, nutrient-packed smoothies.

## Does kale give you eagle eyes and super strength?

Leafy green vegetables like kale are the most nutrient dense foods on earth, and unfortunately they are missing in modern diets. Cruciferous vegetables like kale are the most powerful anti-cancer foods available. Kale's cell wall houses an enzyme, called myrosinase, that is released when the cell wall is opened, creating new compounds that improve our immune defenses and our body's miraculous self-repair mechanisms. Both blending and finely chopping kale releases its full potential. Eating raw leafy greens in salad form also provides numerous nutrients. Just remember to chew them well.

**Vision:** Leafy greens are rich in antioxidants called carotenoids, specifically lutein and zeaxanthin, which are the only carotenoids known to be involved in vision. When we eat leafy greens, lutein and zeaxanthin travel to the retina and filter light, an important process for healthy vision.

**Strength:** Although our culture usually associates protein with meat and dairy, green vegetables actually get the majority of their calories from proteins that are also packaged with beneficial phytochemicals. The protein in green leaves gives us raw material from which we can build muscle when we exercise. Compounds found in green vegetables have been shown to improve muscular endurance and enhance lung function, leading to improved athletic performance.

## Why does Mitch Spinach use white beans in his Dinosaur Soup?

Beans and other legumes, like peas and lentils, are among the world's most perfect foods and the most nutrient-dense carbohydrate sources. Because beans are digested slowly, they stabilize blood sugar (helping to prevent diabetes) and satisfy your appetite for a long period of time (helping you to lose weight). Plus, beans can even lower cholesterol levels! Beans are unique foods because of their high levels of soluble fiber and resistant starch, which help to keep the digestive system healthy and prevent and fight colon cancer. Eating beans, peas, or lentils at least twice a week has been found to decrease colon cancer risk by 50%.

## Mitch Spinach says that he puts nuts and seeds in his super bars. Why?

Nuts and seeds contain healthy fats and a wide variety of nutrients: phytosterols, which lower cholesterol; arginine, which helps to lower blood pressure; minerals; and antioxidants. Nuts are extremely important for keeping the cardiovascular system (heart and blood vessels) healthy, maintaining a healthy weight, and preventing diabetes. The nutritional profile of seeds is similar to that of nuts, but seeds are also abundant in trace minerals and higher in protein than nuts. Flax, chia, and hemp seeds are extremely rich sources of omega-3 fats, which are healthy for the brain and heart. Sunflower seeds are especially rich in protein and minerals. Hemp seeds are rich in protein, and pumpkin seeds are rich in iron and calcium. Sesame seeds have the greatest amount of calcium of any food in the world (more than milk) and provide abundant amounts of vitamin E. Both nuts and seeds promote strength and endurance, as they enhance human lifespan. The healthy fats in nuts and seeds help us to absorb the nutrients in vegetables, and it is best to consume them in their natural, raw form, not roasted or salted. For growing children or those athletes who need extra calories or want to add muscle, eating more nuts and seeds can meet these muscular and caloric needs.

## SOME SECRETS ABOUT A FEW OF THE CHARACTERS IN THIS BOOK

**Mr. Fava** is named after the fava bean, which is also called broad bean, pigeon bean, or horse bean, a bean rich in the minerals manganese, calcium, and phosphorus. They can be cooked and eaten in the pod, but most commonly the beans are shelled first—they can be either boiled like other beans or baked and eaten. When cooking fresh fava, they should be shelled and then boiled to remove the skin.

**Ms. Radicchio** is named after a burgundy leafed vegetable said to be native to Italy. It is often used in salads and has a crunchy, nutty, pleasantly bitter taste that mellows when cooked. Radicchio is a rich source of dietary fiber, antioxidants, vitamins, and minerals.

**Mrs. Persimmon's** name comes from a delicious red-orange fruit originally grown chiefly in Asia, rich in vitamins, minerals, and the proanthocyanidin class of antioxidants, which has anti-cancer and longevity benefits. The skin of the persimmon is also edible, nutritious, and delicious, so eat the entire fruit, except the green stem.

**Principal Lycopene** is named after a very efficient antioxidant responsible for the red pigment found in tomatoes, guava, pink grapefruit and watermelon. Lycopene can neutralize oxygen-derived free radicals that can cause damage to the body and are linked to many degenerative diseases, such as cardiovascular diseases, premature aging, cancer (especially prostate cancer), and cataracts.

# Dinosaur Kale  Soup *(serves 3 - 4)*

## INGREDIENTS

1 bay leaf

1 small onion, chopped

2 celery stalks, diced

1 carrot, chopped

2 cups carrot juice

4 cups no salt vegetable broth (or no-salt bouillon with water)

1 1/2 cup white beans

1 bunch Dinosaur Kale (also called Tuscan or Lacinato Kale), chopped finely, ribs removed

## DIRECTIONS

In medium soup pot or saucepan, sweat onions, celery, carrot, and bay leaf with a tablespoon or two of broth for one minute.

Add carrot juice and broth. You may use any ratio of broth to juice, using all juice or all broth, if you'd like. The carrot juice creates a sweeter and more nutrient-rich soup.

Bring to a boil, then lower heat, cover, and simmer for 15-20 minutes.

Add the beans and the kale and simmer uncovered for 5-10 minutes more.

Remove bay leaf *(see Fun Tip above)* and serve—or send to school in an insulated soup jar.

For more great recipes, nutrition information, games, and Mitch Spinach secrets go to

**www.MitchSpinach.com**